PASS IT ON

LIKE YOU'VE **NEVER** READ THEM BEFORE

ANTHONY HOROWITZ · KEV F SUTHERLAND
MARTIN COLEMAN · GAVIN TYTE · SIR ANDREW MOTION

Bible Society
Trinity Business Centre
Stonehill Green, Westlea
Swindon SN5 7DG

biblesociety.org.uk

This edition published 2015 by The British and Foreign Bible Society

ISBN: 978-0-564-09096-9

Production by Bible Society Resources Ltd, a wholly-owned
subsidiary of The British and Foreign Bible Society
Design by Claire Simmons-Clark
Cover illustrations © 2015 Kev F Sutherland

Printed in Great Britain
BSRL/50M/2015

INTRODUCTION

For as long as there have been people, there have been stories. We all love stories, whether they're long or short, happy or sad, serious or silly. We are inspired by stories of hope and touched by stories of disappointment. Some love fantastical stories of dragons and wizards, princesses and magical lands. Others prefer tales of rags-to-riches, heroes-to-zeroes, quests, rescues and thrilling adventures. And in many ways, your own life is a story!

So we've invited five great storytellers to each choose a story from one of the greatest collections ever known: the Bible.

Each one has retold their story in a different style. In this special collection you will find a short tale, a comic strip, a rhyme, a rap and a poem.

BIBLE CHALLENGE
THE PRIZE

We want you to be a great storyteller too. After you have read the book, why not have a go at writing your own retelling of a Bible story? You can choose whatever style you like. You might want to draw a comic strip, write a poem, or just write a simple story. It's entirely up to you.

You can choose one of the stories that are already in this book or pick your own from the Bible.

To help you decide here are a few suggestions...

Adam and Eve (Genesis 2–3)
Two people, one garden, one snake and one tree with some tasty-looking fruit. What could possibly go wrong?

Noah's Ark (Genesis 6–9)
A lone boat bobs in the ocean. Its crew and cargo are all that's left. How will they rebuild? If the rain ever stops, that is.

Moses and the 10 Commandments (Exodus 19–20)
Terrifying thunder and lightning swirl around a mountain. Only the people's leader dares to climb up. He speaks with God.

David and Goliath (1 Samuel 17)
A giant faces down an entire army. No one will challenge him – until a young shepherd boy steps up...

Queen Esther (Esther 1–8)
A cruel advisor persuades his king to crush a group of people. Is there anyone in a position to save them?

The birth of Jesus *(Luke 1–2)*
A baby is born in a tiny town – happens all the time. So why is the sky exploding with angels?

Mary and Martha *(Luke 10)*
What do you do when Jesus comes round for dinner? As one woman frets to get everything ready, her sister just … sits there.

The story of the lost son *(Luke 15)*
A man stays home and works hard. His brother runs off and ends up homeless, starving and poor. What happens when he comes back?

That's a handful of stories but there are hundreds more in the Bible. If you don't know how to get hold of a copy then ask your parents or guardians. There may be one in your school library or you can also find it on the internet. We suggest you look for the Good News version as it is easy to read.

If you decide to follow in the footsteps of Anthony Horowitz or any of our other authors by rewriting a Bible story, we've got great news.

We're running a competition. Send us your retelling of a Bible story and you could win a fantastic prize. Just submit your story at biblesociety.org.uk/passiton. We will pick the best entry and the winner will receive an iPad and see their story illustrated and framed by *The Beano's* Kev F Sutherland.

To enter, please go to the website
biblesociety.org.uk/passiton

Entry rules and terms and conditions can be found there.

Anthony Horowitz is the author of the number one bestselling Alex Rider books and The Power of Five series. Anthony was also chosen by the Ian Fleming estate to write the new James Bond novel (2015). In 2014 Anthony was awarded an OBE for Services to Literature. He has also created and written many major television series, including *Injustice*, *Collision* and the award-winning *Foyle's War*.

Hannah Hunter-Kelm is an illustrator and printmaker based in Leeds. Her illustrations are primarily made using indian ink and watercolours, drawn with her left hand (even though she is usually right-handed!). Her favourite things to draw are birds, sea creatures, and made up monsters of all shapes and sizes. She recently illustrated a book on parenting visually impaired children for Bethel China, a charity which aims to see children with visual impairments living life to the fullest.

Kev F Sutherland is probably best known as a writer and artist for comics as diverse as *The Beano* — for whom he does Bananaman and Pansy Potter — and Marvel comics, as well as *Doctor Who* and most points in between.

Martin Coleman decided to take seriously his lifelong passion for writing, following a 30-year career in entertainment. His first rhyming children's book, *The King's Panto* was released in 2011 to critical acclaim and this was soon followed by *The Greedy Crocodile* and *The (not quite so) Good Princess*. In 2014 Martin was commissioned by Bible Society to rewrite several stories for their Bible Bedtime apps.

Tim Slater is a freelance Illustrator, who works with pencil and paper before using the computer to add the finishing touches. Born and brought up in Greater Manchester, Tim went on to study Illustration and Visual Communication at Loughborough University. After graduating in 2003, Tim went on to further study at Manchester City College in a bid to embrace the age of digital design.

 **Revd Gavin Tyte** is known as the 'beatboxing vicar'. As well as being an ordained minister in the Church of England he is also a pioneer in the world of beatboxing (vocal percussion). He is author of *The Hip-hop Gospel of Luke*, created the word's first beatboxing video tutorials and is a regular judge at the UK Beatbox Championships.

 **Claire Simmons-Clark's** passion for illustration started at a young age when she became obsessed with books — literally taking a book everywhere she went (still reading some of those books to her children now). Claire has been working in illustration and design since 2000. Whilst studying her degree, Claire won the Reader's Digest prize for Illustration. Claire tries to incorporate elements of humour into her illustrations, adding little surprises for those of the most observant nature.

 **Sir Andrew Motion** was Poet Laureate from 1999 to 2009. He is now Professor of Creative Writing at Royal Holloway. He is a Fellow of the Royal Society of Literature. He was knighted for his services to literature in 2009. He has written many collections of poems such as: *The Customs House; Love in a Life; The Price of Everything*. He has also written novels including *Silver — Return to Treasure Island* and *The Invention of Dr Cake*.

Photographer Charlotte Knee

The Tower of Babel

Genesis 11.1–9

Anthony Horowitz

Author of:
James Bond novel
Alex Rider series

Illustrated by

Hannah Hunter-Kelm

HAVE YOU EVER WONDERED why people all over the world speak different languages? The Bible has an explanation which concerns an extraordinary construction which came to be known as the Tower of Babel.

This all happened some years after the Great Flood which had lasted for one hundred and fifty days, wiping out everyone except for Noah, his family and the animals that went into the ark. For a long time, the world was a terrible mess with puddles everywhere but finally things dried out and humankind began to re-establish itself. Soon, there were thousands of men, women and children and they decided to live together in a beautiful place known as the Land of Shinar which may or may not have been somewhere near Iraq. The Bible is rather vague about the precise location but then it was written a very long time ago. Anyway, everyone was extremely happy. They had olive trees, dates, fig trees, camels, goats, fresh drinking water, peace and perfect weather.

And, at this time, they all spoke the same language.

The trouble started when someone decided to build the biggest, tallest tower that had ever been seen. The Bible doesn't actually tell us who this person was but many scholars point the finger at King Nimrod, a rather cruel and self-important figure who happened to be the great grandson of old Noah himself. Like many tyrants, he was always showing off and he thought that, by building a tower that reached as far as heaven itself, he would prove to the people that he was as powerful as God. It never occurred to him that a vast structure, several miles wide and even more miles high would be completely useless in the middle of the desert and that actually schools, hospitals and community centres would have been a much better bet. No. He called together his architects and engineers and set to work on this fantastic scheme — and even though they would have to do all the heavy lifting and carrying, not one of his people complained.

Very quickly, the Tower of Nimrod began to rise and it really was an amazing sight. It looked a little bit like a wedding cake only it was pale yellow, not white, and actually broke through the clouds.

It had hundreds of thousands of archways all the way round and behind the archways there were doors and windows, corridors and staircases. There were slanting roofs, domes and steeples. In fact, if you can imagine every great building you've ever seen, jumbled together and piled on top of each other, you'll still only be halfway there. (There's actually quite a good picture of it by a man called Peter Bruegel. Do go and look at it if you ever happen to be in Vienna.)

Of course, there were no modern materials. The tower was made of bricks, stone and clay and as cement hadn't been invented yet, the builders stuck it all together with slime which they pulled out of the sea. Because of the huge

weight, it sank deep into the sand but that was probably for the best as it helped the whole thing stay upright.

Now God had watched all this with a certain amount of dismay. It wasn't just that Nimrod was unpleasant and annoying. He saw that human beings, if left to themselves, could waste their time doing all sorts of stupid things. It was all very well people wanting to build and to make their lives better but they really had to think about what they were doing. What they needed to do was to slow down. And that gave God an idea. One night, while everyone was asleep, He acted. In exactly one trillionth of a second, he changed the way they spoke.

So when they all woke up the next day, everyone found that they were talking in a different language.

"Good morning," one builder said to another.
"Buenos dias," replied the second (in Spanish).
"Bună dimineața," cried out a third (in Rumanian).
"Merhaba!" (Turkish)
"Sawubona" (Zulu)
"Was ist los?"[1] asked one of the architects (in German).
"Je n'en ai pas la moindre idée!"[2] replied the assistant chief engineer (in French).
"为什么每个人都在说这么奇怪?"[3] demanded the deputy director of slime (in Chinese).

This went on for some time. In fact, by late afternoon, nobody had done any work and King Nimrod came rushing down to the building site with fury in his eyes.

"Why is nobody working?" he screamed.

But nobody understood a word he was saying either.

[1] "What is wrong?"   [2] "I haven't got the faintest idea."   [3] "Why is everyone talking so strangely?"

And that was about it. Not one more brick of the Tower of Nimrod was laid. After a while, people got fed up and drifted away and after that, nature took over. The winds blew and the desert sun beat down and bit by bit the gigantic structure crumbled and fell down. Nobody knows what happened to King Nimrod although he was always referred to as "Nimrod the Evil" after that and, many thousands of years later, had a long-range air to surface missile (the Nimrod) named after him.

His masterwork is never called the Tower of Nimrod, by the way. It was given the name the Tower of Babel after *balal*, a Hebrew word meaning confused. Or you could say that everyone spoke the same language until it was built but babbled ever afterwards — which is most certainly true.

SAMSON'S PHILISTINE WIFE

JUDGES 14-15

KEV F SUTHERLAND

WRITER AND ILLUSTRATOR:
THE BEANO
BANANAMAN
MARVEL COMICS
DOCTOR WHO

SAMSON'S PHILISTINE WIFE

JUDGES 14-15
AS TOLD BY
KEV F

MUM? DAD? I'VE SEEN A *WOMAN* IN *TIMNAH!* GET HER FOR ME AS MY *WIFE!*

A *PHILISTINE?*

YES. *AND?*

IS THERE *NO* WOMAN AMONG THE DAUGHTERS OF YOUR *BRETHREN?* OR AMONG *MY* PEOPLE?

NOPE. NOPE.

NOT LISTENING

GET HER FOR *MEEE!*

OKAY OKAY

HERE WE ARE SON, THE VINEYARDS OF *TIMNAH*

OOH, WHAT'S *THIS?*

HELLO LITTLE FELLA, WHAT'S *YOUR* NAME?

ROAR!!

UH OH!

SPIRIT OF THE LORD! COMING UPON ME!

REND

THERE YOU GO! TORN *APART* AS YOU MIGHT TEAR APART A YOUNG *GOAT!*

AND *NOTHING* IN MY *HANDS!* YOU'RE *WELCOME*

YOU PLEASE SAMSON *WELL*

I PLEASE *WHO?*

SAMSON. THAT'S *ME*

O... *KAY.* THANKS

YES, SHE PLEASES ME *RIGHT* WELL. MUST REMEMBER TO ASK HER *NAME.* OH *LOOK,* THAT *LION* I KILLED *EARLIER...*

WELL I NEVER *DID!*

BEES MAKING *HONEY* IN MY *CARCASS?* AS IF THIS WASN'T HUMILIATING *ENOUGH!*

BUZZ *OFF!* I'M HAVING SOME OF THAT *HONEY!*

RIGHT! SEVEN DAY WEDDING FEAST!

SEVEN *DAYS?*

IT'S WHAT WE *DO*

LET ME POSE A *RIDDLE* TO ALL OF YOU LOT. *SOLVE* IT BEFORE THE END OF THE *FEAST* AND YOU GET *THIRTY NEW SUITS.* IF YOU *CAN'T,* YOU GIVE *ME* THIRTY NEW SUITS!

GO *ON* THEN

OUT OF THE *EATER* CAME SOMETHING TO EAT, OUT OF THE STRONG CAME SWEETNESS!

SOLVE THAT!

TOUGH ONE!

HE'S GOT ME STUMPED!

WE'RE THIRTY SUITS DOWN ON THIS DEAL AND NO MISTAKE!

HOY! SAMSON'S WIFE!

I DO HAVE A NAME, YOU KNOW!*

* YES, BUT NO-ONE BOTHERED TO WRITE IT DOWN. SORRY - ED

GET YOUR HUSBAND TO EXPLAIN THAT RIDDLE OR WE'LL BURN DOWN YOU AND YOUR DAD'S HOUSE! WITH FIRE!

AND YOU'RE FROM MY SIDE OF THE FAMILY?

2

BY THE WAY, THE 'WITH FIRE' BIT WAS UNNECESSARY

WHATEVER! DO IT!

SO...

OH SAMSON! MY HUSBAND!

WHAT IS IT NOW?

YOU ONLY HATE ME! YOU DO NOT LOVE ME!

YOU'VE POSED THIS RIDDLE BUT NOT EXPLAINED IT TO ME!

I'VE NOT EXPLAINED IT TO MY MUM & DAD EITHER. SO?

BOO HOO! WEEP! WAIL! CRY! MOAN! SCREAM! SNIFFLE

WAAAAAAH! GNASH OF TEETH! WAIL! WEEP! MOAN! SIGH! ULULATE

BOO HOO... I CAN KEEP THIS UP FOR A FULL SEVEN DAYS

OKAY! I'LL TELL YA! I'LL TELL YA!

SO, YOU BUNCH OF PHILISTINES, THE FEAST'S NEARLY UP AND NO-ONE'S SOLVED MY RIDDLE. SO...

ER, IF I MAY...

WHAT IS SWEETER THAN HONEY? WHAT IS STRONGER THAN A LION?

THAT'LL BE THIRTY SUITS WHEN YOU'RE READY

SPIRIT OF THE LORD!

COMING UPON ME!

IF YOU HADN'T PLOWED WITH MY HEIFER* YOU WOULDN'T HAVE SOLVED MY RIDDLE!!

OOOOOOOOOOOH!

SEXIST

*YOU MIGHT WANT TO LOOK THAT UP — ED

3

TO BE CONTINUED...

22

Daniel and the Lions

Daniel 6.1–28

Martin Coleman

Author:
The King's Panto
The Greedy Crocodile
The (not quite so) Good Princess

Illustrated by
Tim Slater

I'll tell you the tale of a very good man,
in a faraway land long ago.
He was gentle and kind, noble and wise,
(there wasn't much he didn't know),
But he lived in a time when if you did a crime,
you weren't just locked up in irons,
Oh no, if the King thought you did a bad thing,
you were thrown in a pit with the lions!

Now this man was clever and worked really hard,
so hard that he rose to great things,
So great in fact, that he was employed
by one or two prominent Kings!
His name was Daniel, a jolly good chap
in every possible way,
And Daniel prayed not once, not twice,
but several times a day!

He'd always face Jerusalem,
(his home town he missed a whole bunch).
He prayed in the morning, he prayed before bed,
and sometimes when having his lunch!
But some of the guys who weren't half as wise,
but were jealous of Daniel's position,
Created a plan to catch out our man,
with their own made-up 'King's inquisition'.

So they convinced 'the boss' that it would be his loss
if his subjects weren't praying to him,
And he made a new rule that you'd be a fool
if you prayed to a god, not the King!
The thing is they knew that Daniel was true
to his God and he just wouldn't change,
And sooner or later he'd get caught out,
so his punishment they could arrange!

So without warning, the very next morning,
they went to his window and hid.
When Daniel awoke, he knelt down and spoke
to God as he usually did.
But he opened his eyes and to his surprise
the men were all there in his room!
"Caught you!" they said as they grabbed him and led
him away to face his doom!

Frightened and shaken, Daniel was taken
in front of the King by the men.
"He's guilty!" they said as he hung his head,
"Throw him in the lion's den!"
The King felt so bad, he was fond of our lad,
but he had to stick to the law,
So he waved his hand and gave the command
to open up the cage door.

Once again he was grabbed by the men
and pushed and shoved and beaten.
The lions were pacing and Daniel was facing
his death by being eaten!
And that evening when he was thrown in the den,
laughing, the men walked away,
Knowing for sure that as he hit the floor
Daniel had seen his last day.

Unable to sleep, the King tried to keep
from thinking of what he had done,
He knew he'd been tricked by these men who had picked
on the man he considered a son.
When morning broke, the King rushed and spoke
to the darkness inside the den,
"Forgive me!" he wept, "I have not slept,
for I know I've betrayed you my friend!"

But although he hurried, he needn't have worried
as there in the shadows he found
The lions asleep, not making a peep
and Daniel quite safe and sound!
"My man, you're alive! How did you survive?"
asked the King in a state of alarm.
"I simply prayed and the lions all stayed
away and caused me no harm."

The King, so relieved now firmly believed
that Daniel was saved by God
And turned the key to set him free
then turned to the guards with a nod.
"Bring me those men who put Dan in the den,
claiming that he was the sinner,
Tell them from me that it's their turn to see
what it feels like to be a cat's dinner!"

So Daniel stayed in his job and he prayed
to God as he always had.
The King was his friend and never again
did he mistake good men for bad.
He wrote a decree for his people to see
that Daniel's God was true.
And I'm so glad to know that now they don't throw
folk to the lions, aren't you?

JONAH THE MOANER

JONAH 1–4

GAVIN TYTE

**WRITER AND PERFORMER:
THE HIP-HOP GOSPEL OF LUKE**

ILLUSTRATED BY
CLAIRE SIMMONS-CLARK

INTRODUCTION

Welcome to the story about a loner called Jonah.

He'll be shown and he'll be known as a bit of a moaner.

But it's not just a ditty about a desperate God escaper,

It's a tale that explains the very nature of the Maker.

So take a seat and stay awake as this yarn is spun,

Let's dive in at the beginning reading Chapter One.

1. JONAH RUNS FROM GOD

The family line is vital for a Jewish guy,
So kicking off, Jonah's dad was tagged as Amittai.
Amittai means 'truth' and Jonah means 'dove'
And a dove is a bringer of love from above.

GOD SPEAKS TO JONAH

Now a bolt from the blue of God's word occurred,
Get a lock on this shocker that Jonah heard,
"I've spotted a problem, a hornet's nest to address,
That Nineveh city's in a bit of a mess.
So behold, I've resolved to get this problem solved
By selecting and electing you to get involved.
You're my man on a mission with a message to impart;
Tell the Ninevites it's time for them to make a fresh start."
But Jonah disagreed and made a mighty quick exit;
Bags packed, roof racked, the lad off and legged it.

So on the run from God he fled south to Joppa
And bought a single trip ticket on the Med non-stopper,
Heading west for Tarshish on a voyage of defection,
A two thousand mile sail in the opposite direction.

GOD SENDS A STORM

Then the Lord sent a storm
that could send the boat down.
The waves pounded the ship which
risked running aground.
But the sailors were afraid
and so they knelt and prayed.
They paid respects to their
gods to quickly come to their aid.
And to lighten the freight
they obeyed the captain's code,
Making haste to cast away
the weighty laden payload.
But Jonah'd gone below and
he was safely stowed,
He was power saving batteries
in a deep sleep mode.
So the skipper went to J before the ship
became a wreck
Saying, "How can you sleep?
Get your butt up on the deck!
'Cause it's time to get down on your knees and pray.
Perhaps your God'll take note so we won't be washed away?"

WHO CAUSED THE STORM

Now back in the day, when disaster struck,

With a run of bad luck you had to pass the buck.

So the crew debated who was fated, how to name and shame,

"Let's take aim, cast lots and discover who's to blame!"

They rolled a dice, tossed a coin and who should win the prize draw?

Jonah's name was hat-pulled, Jonah picked the short straw.

Straight away they plied questions and pressurised,

"It's time to whistle-blow the deity that's got us hog-tied!

So tell us your profession, where you're from and your nation.

You've gotta spill the baked-beans about your background situation."

J replied, "I'm a Hebrew so I back the main man,

That's the Lord, God of heaven who made the sea and dry land."

The crew were terrified, afraid, 'cause he was on the run.

J explained, but they campaigned, "What the beep have you done?"

JONAH GETS THROWN OVERBOARD

Meanwhile, the sea was getting rougher,

staying upright getting tougher,

"Tell us what to do to you so that we don't have to suffer?"

So Jonah professed, "If you want to achieve success

Then toss me into the sea and the storm will be suppressed.

It's the only acid test to lay this crisis to rest.

I confess it's my fault for I'm your unwelcome guest!"

But taking to the oars the crew gave it their best

But the hurricane surged like something possessed.

Then the crew beat their breasts, hard pressed and stressed

"Lord, don't let us die as Jonah's death is progressed

He's an innocent man and we beg of you thus,
You've done as you pleased so don't pin it on us!"
So they nabbed and grabbed Jonah who didn't fight arrest.
They threw him overboard, no rubber ring or life vest,
And then straight away as if a wizard waved a magic wand,
The sea was as calm as a farm millpond.
And with conditions restored the crew onboard were awed,
With offerings and vows they bowed and praised the Lord.
So Jonah sank down, it was his time to go,
Blowing bubbles as he flowed to the depths below.
But God supplied a huge fish, he wasn't read his last rites
And it swallowed Jonah whole for three days and three nights.

2. JONAH'S PRAYER

Now, before I go on and you think
I've twisted the tail,
In the original script it was a fish,
not a whale.
And so being turned to fish food
and stuck inside a huge cod,
In a stinking stomach sac Jonah
prayed out loud to God:

"In distress I called on God who tuned in to my cry.

From the depths of the dead I got his fishy reply.

You hurled me deep down to the bottom of the sea,

Currents carried, tides twisted, breakers swept over me.

I said, 'I've been banished, and I'm out of your sight,

But I'll see you once again when this trouble's put right.'

I was swamped and dragged down, my feet were lumps of lead,

Man, I even had seaweed slapped and wrapped around my head!

I sank down to the roots of the mountains off-shore,

No, I couldn't sink lower than the firm sea floor.

But my life was saved and from the depths I've risen

'Cause you busted me out of my undersea prison.

I kept God in my mind as my life was slowly throttled.

My prayers floated upwards like a message in a bottle.

'If you wanna save your life then hold to heaven above.

Don't cling to shoddy idols and ignore God's love.'

So I will meditate and celebrate with grateful praise,

Devout and shouting out that 'our God saves!'

And as I pay my respects I will offer and respond,

Making good on my promise for my word is my bond."

And after J had finished praying the Lord issued a command.

The fish retched and fetched him up, spewing J on dry land.

3. JONAH OBEYS GOD

Then God was on repeat, his looping rap had never changed.

He dictated and restated and related again,

"Time to pack up your bags and go to Nineveh town

To announce the state of play and the law I've laid down."

JONAH PREACHES IN NINEVEH CITY

So Jonah agreed, book played and obeyed,

But the city was so big that it took him three days.

And after one day of tripping, his record started spinning,

Preaching, "You're out of control and your morals are slipping.

I've started my stopwatch to count down forty days

Then the city will be crushed so amend your ways!"

THE PEOPLE HEAR JONAH

Jonah's words rang true and the people saw the light.

The Ninevites, that night, began a hunger strike.

As a sign to the Divine, right down the line,

Dressing up in old sacks became the vogue design.

THE KING OF NINEVEH ISSUES A ROYAL DECREE

Now being told of Jonah's omen the king listened and took note.

He rose up from his throne, unclothed and disrobed.

And getting the message and the cut and the thrust,

He sack wrapped himself up and sat down in the dust.

Then making and dictating a notification,

He royally announced this public information:

"By order of the king and his sovereign crew

You've gotta show that you're sorry, let me tell you what to do.

Not you, not your dog, cat, chickens or herds

Are allowed to eat or drink 'cause action's louder than words.

Every person and every creature will have to don the sack,

'Cause it's time to plead with God and get your lives back on track.

No more breaking the law in the Nineveh locality.

Give up your wrongdoing and your wicked brutality.

And with God's anger burning and our conscience returning,

Concerning our fate the Lord might be U-turning.

And you're never, ever knowing, he might start showing

Some pity for the city and let his mercy start flowing?"

THE PEOPLE OBEY AND GOD RELENTS

The crowds listened to the message and inwardly digested,

Then they dressed in sacks exactly as the king had requested.

Now when the Lord God surveyed how they'd changed their ways,

He put a stop to Plan A and he re-appraised.

He saw how the people had been good and behaved,

So he didn't bring destruction and the city was saved.

4. JONAH MOANS

But Jonah got all angry and his mood was dark.

He thought that God was all wrong and acting way off the mark.

So he raised his eyes to the sky and began to vent,

"I told you this would happen, it's what I tried to prevent!

That's why I made my escape and evaded your request

I took to Tarshish because I second-guessed

What would happen, what you're like — you love and don't ration it.

You're full of mercy, kind and compassionate.

You're always slow to anger and you long to hold back,

Taking up the slack, you don't want to attack.

Now, Lord, take my life and put a gun to my head.

I don't want to be alive 'cause I'd be better off dead!"

GOD GETS THROUGH TO JONAH USING A STRANGE PLANT

But the Lord God replied, taking Jonah to one side,

Asking, "Do you have the right to be so angry inside?"

You see, Jonah'd set up camp to the east of the town,

And in the shelter, home-made, in the shade he sat down.

With a grand-stand position, to witness God's mission,

Jonah sat, watched and waited for the city's demolition.

And as J was hot sweating, the Lord came to his aid.

The Lord raised a strange plant to give Jonah more shade.

Being relieved by the tree and with his sunburn eased,

He was appeased, feeling glee, care free and pleased.

But at the break of day God provided a worm

Which in turn, chewed for food and went and withered the fern.

And when the sun returned, God provided a scorcher;

Solar wind and blazing rays, a baking oven of torture.

And as his brain began to boil, J began to fade and faint

No restraint and true to form Jonah vented his complaint,

"I wanna curl up and die!" he cried, "there's no misgiving!

Listen up, take it in, I'm saying dying beats living!"

GOD CHALLENGES JONAH

But God said to Jonah, "I can hear you blurbing.

Is it right for you to find that plant so disturbing?"

"Yes it is!" J replied, and then he went on and said,

"I'm so angry, seeing red, that I wish I were dead!"

GOD EXPLAINS ABOUT THE PLANT

"You're concerned about a plant you didn't seed or even sow.
You didn't tend it or water it or make the thing grow.
It sprouted overnight and it quickly flowered.
It lived and died within twenty-four hours.
So don't you reckon, for a second, I should be concerned
If the great city of Nineveh stands or burns?
It numbers a hundred and twenty thousand strong,
Full of animals and people that don't know right from wrong."

OUTRODUCTION

So that was the story about a loner called Jonah.
You can see why he was known as a bit of a moaner.
But it wasn't just a ditty about a desperate God escaper,
It was tale that explained the very nature of the Maker.
So I hope you stayed awake as this yarn was spun,
We've read the whole story and now we're done.

Triptych

Matthew 4.1–11
John 11.1–44
Mark 14.12–26

Sir Andrew Motion

Poet Laureate 1999–2009

Illustrated by
Hannah Hunter-Kelm

1. IN THE WILDERNESS

What does a man see
in the wilderness
if not a reed shaken by the wind?

Since I arrived here
I have admired thousands
for the music they produce –

astringent in summer,
in winter fuller and nearly sweet
thanks to the green moisture in the leaf.

As for human visitors
and their wish to get in touch,
there has only been this stranger,
who if he spoke at all
argued with his shadow.

So far as I can tell
nothing altered when he went.

I still bathe myself in streams
poured out by the desert lark;

I read the news I need
in the footprints of lizards

and the looping hieroglyphics
snakes leave with their skin.

2. LAZARUS

I slipped over the border.

I fell down into the pure dark
with no dreaming.

Then I came home again.

Wherever I go now –
to market in the village,
or brushing through the fields at harvest –
I like to imagine
I leave swirling trails of light.

In truth there is nothing so obvious
to show me unlike
the man I was before.

And yet to speak in confidence
I am almost worn through
by the terms of my existence.

They require me to raise my voice
every single day
and declare that I am happy.

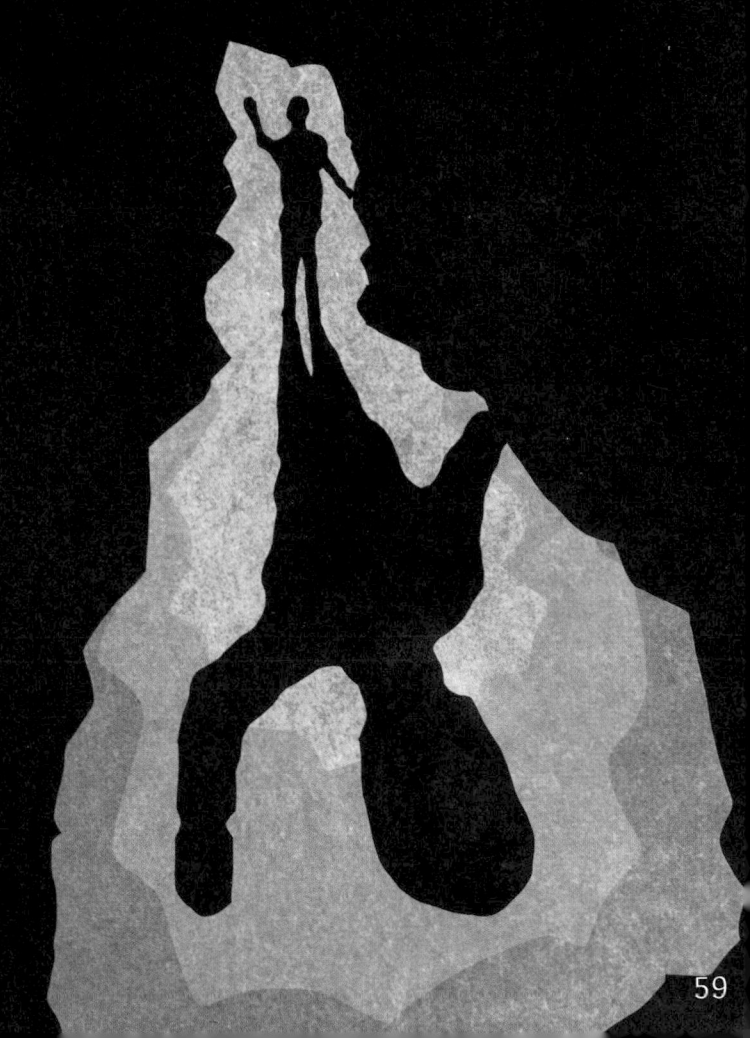

3. THE UPPER ROOM

My task is to clear the room
when the guests go home at night.

To straighten the benches,

to sweep up the breadcrumbs,
fish skeletons and stalks of peppers,

to separate the olives from the olive stones,

and lastly to wipe away the stain
if any wine has spilt between the pitcher and the cups.

Now you've read the stories in this book why not have a go at writing your own Bible story. This page is for you to get started. When you have found a story you like from the Bible have a think about how you would like to re-tell your story. Remember, you can get creative with the details!

Who have you decided is your main character? What do they look like? What's their personality?

Where do you want it to be set? What does the place look like? Is it set in Biblical times or maybe in the future?

What happens in your story? Are you clear about the beginning the middle and end?

Get scribbling here:

NEED INSPIRATION?

You can choose one of the stories already in this book or pick your own — we've made some suggestions on page 4 but if you're still looking for inspiration you'll need to get hold of a Bible.

There are lots of different versions to choose from. We'd recommend the Good News Bible because it's easy to read and written in modern language.

If you don't have a copy you can buy one from the Bible Society online shop — **biblesociety.org.uk/shop.** You can also try places like Amazon.co.uk or it might be worth checking out your school or local library first. You'll also be able to find the Good News translation on the internet.